M|C|C

LICENTIATE
to HEAL

A History of the Medical Council of Canada

CHRISTY VODDEN

Library and Archives Cataloguing:
Vodden, Christy
Licentiate to Heal: A History of the Medical Council of Canada

Issued also in French under the title:
Médecins à juste titre : Bref historique du Conseil médical du Canada

ISBN: 978–0–9690161–8–2

Published by the
Medical Council of Canada
2283 St. Laurent Blvd.
Ottawa, Ontario K1G 3H7

Design: Tracy Carefoot Visual
Translation: Hélène Cloutier-Carty
Printer: Canton Print Limited
Indexer: Elizabeth Macfie

Printed in Canada.

TABLE *of* CONTENTS

INTRODUCTION

The Medical Council of Canada occupies a unique role at the interface between the graduating medical student and the practising physician. It provides the only formal forum for the educational institutions and the regulatory authorities of the medical community. Both groups are integral to assuring high standards of competence for those who are allowed to practise medicine in Canada, and since 1912, as prescribed by the Canada Medical Act, they have been coming annually to the Medical Council's table to debate this very question – and always with the underlying purpose of improving care to Canadians.

As the Medical Council closes in on its centennial anniversary, what better time to take a look back at where we have come from, so as to better appreciate where we are now, and inform our discussions about where we should be heading? The journey has not always been an easy one, nor could it have been, nor will it be, given the complexity of our country with its often uneasy balancing act between provincial and national interests. Our founder, Sir Thomas Roddick, certainly found that out during his 18-year campaign to get agreement on the legislation and regulations for a national qualification in medicine that would be acceptable to the provinces for the issuance of a licence to practise within their boundaries. And even before Roddick took up this monumental challenge, there was a 27-year period of debate on the topic, at just about every meeting of the Canadian Medical Association from its founding in 1867.

Thousands of people have been part of the Medical Council of Canada and furthered its work over the past century. In that number, we have had more than a healthy share of leaders, visionaries, tireless workers, passionate spokespersons and outright characters. An entire book could, and should, be written about the test committees for our examinations – the suggested title "Unsung Heroes." The practitioners and educators, who have toiled on these committees over the years reviewing and fine-tuning the questions, are a key component of the Medical Council's intellectual infrastructure.

Through all our efforts, there are now well over 100,000 names inscribed in the Canada Medical Register, which we maintain. Sir Thomas Roddick would be immensely proud of the achievements of the Medical Council of Canada, as should we all.

M. Ian Bowmer, MD CM FRCPC
LMCC No. 30017
Executive Director
Medical Council of Canada

Riddled with "demi-Doctors," negligent, a danger to the public at large… these were some of the attributes of pre-Confederation medical practice according to Archibald Hall, a doctor who contributed to the *Montreal Gazette* in 1842 under the pen name *Medicus*. Indeed, it was widely acknowledged that some of the medications and treatments of general medicine were so drastic during those days that a patient very often had a better chance of living without medical attention than with it.

A share of the blame can be placed squarely on the state of medical education in the late eighteenth and early nineteenth centuries. Doctors trained in Canada during that period did so under an apprenticeship system, there being no requirement for any previous or formal course of study. Students, apprenticed to an established doctor, could very easily end up with a spotty and uneven education. *Medicus* summed it up as: "their knowledge of Anatomy, studied from books as old and antique as may well be imagined, serves them to know, at best, the carotid artery from the femoral, and is utterly unfit for assisting them in the performance of the most trifling operation in Surgery. Their knowledge of Medicine and Surgery, derived from the same source, renders them worse than useless at the bedsides of the sick, from a deficiency of practical information, and serves to confuse, more than enlighten, as to the nature and proper treatment of the disease before them."

Change was rapidly afoot, however, driven by advancements in medicine and by rigorous education curriculum being set for medical students in Europe. In fact, in 1823, it was four Edinburgh-educated doctors, working at the newly opened Montreal General Hospital, who started up Canada's first program of medical education, with the express purpose of offering lectures to students of medicine. In 1829, the Montreal Medical Institution, as it was named, became the Faculty of Medicine at McGill College. Four years later, in 1833, McGill awarded Canada's first Doctor of Medicine and Surgery to William Leslie Logie, who promptly left the country to set up a practice in the United States. In those early days at McGill, instruction was almost exclusively through lectures, with little or no practical demonstrations, and the scientific foundation of modern medicine was not yet in place.

∼∞∞∼

Ensuring professional standards through licensing was another major stumbling block. The need to verify qualifications had been recognized and addressed as early as 1750 in a bill that required anyone wishing to practise in New France to pass an examination set by the King's Doctor. This was followed, in 1788, by an Act that set up an examining board of elected licensed physicians. The core of the problem is encapsulated in the amending legislation passed in Lower Canada in 1831 "to provide more effectual regulations concerning the practice of Physic, Surgery, and Midwifery." This Act paid great attention to the nuts and bolts of setting up a medical board, detailing its regulations and prescribing the penalties to be inflicted upon those practising without a licence. What the Act failed to do was say anything whatsoever about education standards for doctors. Ironically, though, it set stringent regulations for apothecaries and required them to have "a proper preliminary education." But not a word about any formal education requirements for doctors! The legislative groundwork in Upper Canada was in a similar state, with Acts governing registration and licensing passed in 1827 and 1839, the latter being disallowed owing to objections from the Royal College of Physicians and Surgeons of London on the grounds that it infringed their rights.

The country doctor of years past has become a mythic figure in Canada – a symbol of dedication, selflessness and hard work in all types of weather. This is a well-deserved tribute in many respects, but the competence and skills of Canada's early doctors ranged from excellent to outright quackery. Pre-Confederation medical education offered little formal curriculum and was mainly the result of apprenticeship, a system totally dependent upon the skill of the teaching doctor and the time he had or cared to give to instruction. And perish the thought that the country doctor should drive his buggy across a provincial boundary to treat someone on the other side, unless he had applied for a licence to practise there!

In 1841, the union of Upper and Lower Canada (constituting those parts of present-day Quebec and Ontario along the shores of the St. Lawrence and Great Lakes) created a single government for a new Province of Canada. The first sitting of its legislature was a busy one, and education was amongst the major issues on the agenda – in fact, one of the bills introduced was aimed specifically at medical education. Although it had the support of the medical profession, the legislators referred it to a committee, where it was altered so much that it was no longer acceptable to anyone and was subsequently thrown out of the House. A much-watered down Act was later passed, but it was really just an exercise in legal paperwork required to specify that previously issued licences were valid in the new Province of Canada. These practitioners, however, were still subject "to the Laws of the place in which they practise," meaning a previously licensed physician in Lower Canada would still need to seek a licence from the Medical Board of Upper Canada to practise there, and vice versa.

Medical boards were well established by the time that the Province of Canada came into being. There were ones for Upper Canada, Montreal and Quebec City, and they were trying to address some issues of mutual concern. In 1847, the Medical Board of Upper Canada negotiated an agreement with the Montreal and Quebec boards to set in place a uniform system of examination for candidates applying to any of them, as well as a mutual exchange of the names of rejected candidates, the reasons for their rejection and the period set for them to continue their studies before presenting themselves for re-examination.

So the situation by Confederation, which on July 1, 1867 added the British provinces of New Brunswick and Nova Scotia to the existing Province of Canada and created the Dominion of Canada, was that standards for medical qualifications necessary for a licence to practise were literally all over the map – the new Maritime provinces having their own legislation and medical boards, all with different requirements and standards. One thing that they did share, though, was the lack of any simple mechanism by which a doctor in one province could practise in another. And there was much interest in the medical community to see one put in place.

Sir Charles Tupper, Father of Confederation and future Prime Minister of Canada, was elected as the first President of the Canadian Medical Association at its founding meeting in 1867. He was a strong supporter of the concept of a national portable registration for medical practitioners.

The first to take a big step in that direction was the Medical Society of Quebec. On June 5, 1867, mere weeks in advance of Confederation, it started pushing for a "uniform system of granting licences to practise medicine, surgery and midwifery throughout the Dominion of Canada." A committee, led by William Marsden, issued four recommendations, which, in a nutshell, called for a coming together of the medical profession from across the new Dominion of Canada to thrash out the details. It turned out to be a very lengthy thrashing, ending 45 years later – owing mainly to the British North America Act, which set the ground rules for Confederation and granted exclusive responsibility to the provinces for education, including that of professional groups. The medical community was about to be thrown head first into the federal-provincial power struggle that has been the hallmark of Canadian politics since day one.

2. A CURIOUS COMPLEXITY

The bold call to action issued by the Medical Society of Quebec brought 164 doctors from all parts of the new Dominion to Quebec City for a meeting in October 1867. The result was the founding of the Canadian Medical Association, with Sir Charles Tupper as its first President. Steps were quickly taken to draft a bill entitled the "Medical Act of the Dominion of Canada," which would create a central council of medical education to register all licensed practitioners in Canada. This turned out to be extremely tricky business, riddled with controversy, dissension and questions of legislative legality that raged over the next few years.

By 1872 matters had reached such an impasse that the whole question was deferred for two years. In 1874, it was William Marsden, one of the original proponents of the idea and now President, who had to lay the project to rest, with some regret, saying, "This proposed Act has been a bone of contention, an apple of discord, to the Association ever since it was first introduced." There followed 20 years of relative inactivity on the whole matter, although it was mentioned frequently at Association meetings and some valiant, but generally doomed, attempts were made by the provinces to come to a cooperative understanding through which each would recognize the licence of another. The Maritime Provinces were the most successful and passed legislation in 1894 giving Prince Edward Island, Nova Scotia and New Brunswick, in effect, an inter-provincial licence.

> "The fight to set a uniform level of medical qualifications that would be accepted anywhere in Canada was taken up in 1894 by one Thomas George Roddick…"

As is so often true of causes that wobble along in many directions, their outcome rests upon the person who steps forward to be their champion. In this particular case, fate proved to be very kind. The fight to set a uniform level of medical qualifications that would be accepted anywhere in Canada was taken up in 1894 by one Thomas George Roddick, a larger-than-life personality who combined unstoppable charm with steely determination. In this classic case of immoveable object meeting irresistible force, it was the latter, Roddick, who won out – granted, after some 18 years of effort.

That Roddick, a Newfoundlander by birth, ended up in Canada was a bit of a fluke – and an extremely fortunate one at that. His original intent had been to study medicine in Edinburgh. To get there in 1864, he had to go by way of Montreal, where he followed up on an introduction to George Fenwick, chief surgeon at the Montreal General Hospital. By one of those strange twists of fate, during the visit Fenwick was called away to a train disaster to provide medical assistance, and Roddick offered to go along. His surgical skills and calm-headedness at the accident scene (at which almost 100 people perished) so impressed Fenwick that he convinced Roddick to stay in Montreal and pursue his studies at McGill.

Roddick had a brilliant student career, capped by being chosen class valedictorian. In his speech he exhorted his fellow graduates to "persevere, gentlemen, patiently, ploddingly, persevere." Little did he realize, one suspects, that those words would resonate so profoundly in his own life and categorize perfectly his efforts to set up the Medical Council of Canada.

Licentiate to Heal: A History of the Medical Council of Canada

Thomas Roddick, a native of Harbour Grace, Newfoundland, came to Canada in 1864 to study at McGill. He quickly became one of Montreal's most respected doctors, being one of the first to introduce Lister's antiseptic methods in Canada. He was an influential educator at McGill, Deputy Surgeon-General during the North-West Rebellion, a Member of Parliament, and the founder of the Medical Council of Canada.

Roddick, by all accounts an extremely energetic and fit man, is shown with the Terra Nova Snowshoe Club in 1875 (centre, hand on hip). The photo was produced by the renowned Notman Studio, which was much favoured by Montrealers of means. In 1870, Notman started making these composite photographs, in which everyone was photographed individually in the studio, then the resulting portrait was cut out and pasted into a realistically painted backdrop.

Upon graduation in 1868, Roddick began building an impressive reputation. Of particular note, he helped introduce innovations such as Lister's antiseptic methods to Canadian surgery in the early 1870s, and, in 1885, during the North-West Rebellion, new ways of conducting medicine on the battlefield, including Canada's first hospital train. He began his long association with McGill in 1873, becoming Dean of Medicine in 1901, where he made an indelible contribution by, amongst other things, setting the faculty's funding base on a firm footing and opening the dental school.

In 1894, the Canadian Medical Association, no doubt encouraged by the success of the Maritime Provinces, decided to tackle the matter of national registration one more time, and Roddick was invited to chair the committee charged with the task. So began his 18-year campaign to fight his way through the jungle of what he called Canada's "curious complexity of Medical Legislation" created by the British North America Act. The worst effect of which, to his mind, was that each province had erected the equivalent of a Great Wall of China around its boundary, and each zealously guarded its frontiers so that it was "unsafe for a medical man to pass from one to another unarmed with a licence, because of the risk of fine or even imprisonment."

By this time Canada had expanded considerably with the addition of Manitoba, British Columbia and Prince Edward Island, each of which brought their own unique and divergent brand of legislation, medical boards and licensing requirements to the table. The number of medical schools had grown as well, and they had a most particular interest in registration and professional standards. For example, the charters for Laval, McGill and Bishop's specified that the diplomas they issued were to be accepted by the Quebec licensing body as sufficient to practise medicine in the province, and they considered talk of a national examining board to be an infringement.

Roddick carefully constructed his committee with representatives from all the provinces, and by 1898, after some diplomatic defusing by him of ill feelings amongst various provincial members, the committee produced a report that covered matriculation requirements, professional education and examination standards. It further recommended setting up an "Examining Board for the Dominion" with the examiners appointed by the medical councils of the provinces. Successful candidates were to be entitled to registration in the provinces upon payment of the provincial registration fee. Roddick, who was a Member of Parliament by this time, was to be authorized to take "the necessary steps in the matter." Meaning he was to table it as legislation and push it through. The Canadian Medical Association, given Roddick's careful consensus building during the drafting of the report, was able to send it off to the political arena with its full support.

It was partly through the encouragement of his friend Sir Charles Tupper, Prime Minister for ten weeks in 1896 and leader of the Conservative Party, that Roddick threw his hat into the ring. Tupper had even promised Roddick a Cabinet post. This fit nicely with Roddick's keen interest in seeing the legislation for Dominion registration passed, and his realization that it would require a political champion to shepherd it through the House. As it turned out, Roddick was elected in 1896 by a slim margin of 173 votes, but the majority went to Wilfrid Laurier and his Liberals, in what was a stunning victory that ended the almost unbroken reign of the Conservatives since Confederation.

Roddick was well aware that the passage of a piece of legislation was fraught with hazards, and more so, if it were offered up by a political neophyte sitting in the opposition. So, even though he had the blessing of the Canadian Medical Association, he decided to bide his time and make sure the bill was on a truly sure footing with the provinces before moving forward. He worked tirelessly at this and travelled across the country, addressing medical councils and other professional gatherings, capping it all off in 1899 with a coast-to-coast trip in the company of his friend Sir William Van Horne, then President of the Canadian Pacific Railway.

Roddick's name is the first entry in the Canada Medical Register, a well-deserved honour in recognition of his tireless effort to bring the Medical Council of Canada into being.

3. THE DOCTOR'S BILL

Even Sir Charles Tupper, that seasoned political maestro, did not
think Roddick would get his bill passed. And that was when Tupper
expected the Conservatives to be in power for its journey through the
House! Legislatively it was a slippery dilemma, requiring nothing less than an
amendment to the British North America Act. Roddick, himself, realized that
this route would be impossible. It would need the support of all the provinces,
then the agreement of both the Canadian and British Parliaments – truly, as he
described it, "a large and heavy contract." However, with the help of some legal
friends, Roddick found another way. Section 91 of the British North America
Act granted the right to the Dominion government to make laws "for the peace,
order and good government of Canada in relation to all matters not coming
within the classes of subjects by this Act assigned exclusively to the legislature
of the provinces."

On March 13, 1901, in his speech to table the bill that set in motion "An Act
to Provide for the Establishment of a Medical Council of Canada," Roddick
pointed out to the House of Commons that nothing could be more of a
violation of this "peace, order and good government" than the fact that "a
medical man cannot cross the imaginary line between the provinces without

running the risk of being fined, perhaps imprisoned, when he is attempting to save the lives of citizens of Canada." Roddick also played the reciprocity card, pointing out that Canadian doctors were at a real disadvantage if they wished to work in other countries, as they had no Canadian credentials and the provincial licences were not recognized everywhere. This meant, for example, that a Canadian doctor, unlike those from other British colonies, had to take a year's study or more in Great Britain in order to practise there. In fact, it was bitter gall to the medical community that Canadian doctors attached to the regiments fighting in the South African War, which was raging at that very moment, were not allowed to treat anyone except Canadian soldiers because of these registration issues.

Roddick had had to bide his time in tabling the bill and toe the party line. The Conservatives were the opposition party, and they had their own very particular agenda to squeeze into the limited time available to them. Roddick's platform when he ran for the Montreal-St. Antoine riding did not even mention the issue of Dominion registration. He campaigned on maintaining the protective tariff, increasing trade, strengthening connections with Britain, restoring school privileges to Manitoba Catholics, and bringing Newfoundland into Confederation. His maiden speech in the House of Commons on June 30, 1899, was on measures to control tuberculosis in Canada, and he later spoke on the need for setting up a bureau of public health and was a strong supporter of an anti-smoking motion.

*Licentiate to Heal:
A History of the
Medical Council
of Canada*

Sir Wilfrid Laurier, Prime Minister from 1896-1911, did not support Roddick's bill to establish the Medical Council of Canada when it was first tabled in 1901, but by the third reading, he had been won over. He concluded that it was expedient and logical for the Dominion of Canada's Parliament to "enact a law which we think ought to be passed, but leave it to the provinces themselves to say whether they will be bound by it."

"By the third reading, however, Laurier was a
supporter of the bill, and it was passed
on May 15, 1902 as the Canada Medical Act."

When the bill was finally tabled for its first reading in 1901, sandwiched
between an amendment to the Elections Act and questions about the price of
binder twine, it was as a private member's bill sponsored by Roddick, and it was
clear that Wilfrid Laurier was going to be yet another obstacle in its way. Laurier
originally did not support the bill, nor did he even think that Parliament had
the legal authority to consider it – not to mention that he had had complaints
about it from Quebec constituents. Roddick had trouble convincing Laurier to
put it back on the House agenda for a second reading, which caused a journalist
to quip that this was because "You seldom meet a man who really likes doctors'
bills." The bill finally squeaked in for its second reading, at which point Laurier
was more supportive and agreed to send it to a special committee that would
"look into its merits, and the law as well," although he joked that should the
committee, weighted with medical men, not have a sufficient number of lawyers
on it to "kill the bill", then more could be added. By the third reading, however,
Laurier was a supporter of the bill, and it was passed on May 15, 1902 as the
Canada Medical Act. What clinched the deal was the last-minute inclusion of
an amendment specifying that all the provinces had to pass enabling legislation
before the Act could come into effect.

Manitoba, Nova Scotia and Prince Edward Island quickly passed the necessary
legislation. Some of the others dragged their feet for a decade despite the
concerted efforts and diplomacy of Roddick, who, once again, toured the
country, meeting with the recalcitrant provincial medical councils and
legislatures. Critical of the delaying tactics, the Canadian Medical Association
took up the cause one more time, and in 1909 set up a committee, chaired
by Roddick, to come up with alternatives that would counteract the points
opposed by the hold-out provinces. The resulting amendments included
deleting all references to education requirements, as this was a matter of
provincial responsibility; revising the method of apportioning representation

on the Medical Council; and adding a retroactive clause whereby previously licensed doctors would receive Dominion registration without having to take an examination if they had held those licences for a period of ten years.

Miraculously these were acceptable to all, and the text of the Act was revised accordingly. It was hoped that it could be sent back to Parliament in the winter of 1909, but British Columbia asked for more time so that the amendments could be sent to all of its doctors for final approval, and the homeopaths lobbied successfully for recognition, so clauses covering their system of practice had to be developed. This delayed its tabling by a full year, much to Roddick's consternation. The Act finally went to Parliament on January 23, 1911, shepherded by the Honourable Dr. J.B. Black, M.P. for Hants, as Roddick had not been in Parliament since 1904 when, after two terms in office, he decided not to seek re-election. The "Act to Amend the Canada Medical Act" received Royal Assent on May 19, 1911. British Columbia, Quebec and Ontario, in that order, finally passed the necessary enabling legislation. At long last, all the cats had been successfully herded and corralled. As of April 16, 1912, the date upon which Ontario's legislation was passed, the Medical Council of Canada had all the legal blessings required to set up operations.

Everyone recognized that nothing would have happened at all if not for Thomas Roddick, the remarkable champion who devoted so much time, energy, and even his own money, to make sure that the Medical Council of Canada became a reality. In recognition of his monumental achievement, the Canadian Medical Association, at its meeting in June 1912, paid Roddick the highest tribute within its power, by naming him Honourary President for life.

One of the strong arguments put forth by Roddick in tabling his bill for Dominion registration was that it would address the insulting situation that licences issued by the provinces to Canadian doctors were not recognized by Great Britain, and so Canadian doctors who signed up for the South African War (1899-1902) were restricted to working only on the Canadian wounded.

Chapter

4. DOWN *to* BUSINESS

The Honourable W.J. Roche, Minister of the Interior, representing the Minister of Agriculture under whom all matters pertaining to health fell, opened the Council's first meeting at 10:00 a.m. on November 7, 1912, in an ornate hall in the Parliament Buildings. The very first order of business was the election of the Council's first President, and, fittingly, that honour went to Roddick by unanimous vote. Robert S. Thornton from Manitoba was elected Vice-President, and five others were named to form the Executive Committee.

The Canada Medical Act specified the precise membership of the Council, and this had been one of the most contentious points to resolve. In the end, after having tossed out the idea of provincial representation by population of medical practitioners, the agreed-upon formula was two members appointed by each provincial medical council, one member from each university conferring medical degrees, and three members elected by the homeopathic practitioners. In addition, there were three members appointed by the Governor in Council, each of whom had to come from a different province, with the caveat that two come from Saskatchewan, Alberta or British Columbia until such time as these provinces had medical schools and were eligible for university representation. Roddick and representatives of British Columbia and Alberta were the first three government appointees. In total, there were 32 members on the first Council, and the founding meeting lasted three days. It, in fact, had to be held in two parts, owing to the legality of anything to do with the examinations hinging upon prior approval by the government. As a result, the Council had to reconvene June 17-19, 1913, in order to have time to submit plans for such approval.

Financial considerations were a critical element to pin down, as the Council had no funding base, and part of the first day was spent with the Minister of Finance discussing a government grant to get the Council up and running. They received $15,000, and this was $5,000 shy of what had been requested. The shortfall required immediate scaling back of travel expenses to be paid to Council members. Under the original budget, after paying the meeting and other necessary expenses, the Council would have been stony broke, with nothing left to fund the first examinations. It required some judicious trimming of expense claims to find the money for the examinations.

The Executive Committee's very first decision was to name Robert Powell as the Council's Registrar. His was a pivotal position, ensuring the day-to-day operation of the Medical Council, and one that he held for 16 years. His annual salary was set at $2,000, out of which he was to supply an office and stenographer. Because of the adjournment until June and to conserve funds, Powell's appointment did not take effect until April 1, 1913, during which time Council members A.W.H. Lindsay and J.S. Gray carried out the duties of the Registrar at no cost to the Council. Powell set up the Council's first office in his own home at 180 Cooper Street in Ottawa, between Elgin Street and the Rideau Canal. The Cartier Place Hotel now occupies that address.

An education committee was struck to block out the all-important parameters of the examinations, and they took much care to ensure that everything "should reach the high water mark of efficiency." Everyone at the meeting was painfully aware that the credibility and future acceptance of the Council rested upon this first set of examinations going off without a hitch. To ensure that this would happen, as well as to cope with the limited budget, the Council agreed to hold the first examinations in one place. After much debate Montreal was selected, both for its ease of access for candidates and its pool of English and French-speaking examiners.

The first Council met November 7-9, 1912 in Ottawa. A small Executive Committee was struck to facilitate decision-making between Council meetings. It included W. Spankie (Ontario), E.A.P. Hardy (Homeopaths, Toronto), T.G. Roddick (President, Quebec) and R.S. Thornton (Vice-President, Manitoba), R.E. McKechnie (British Columbia), and L.P. Normand (Quebec). From where the Council stood for this picture they would have been able to see the newly opened Château Laurier, where so many future meetings were to be held.

Two important issues that were to become recurring items of discussion at meetings for years to come were first addressed at the June 1913 meeting: namely, reciprocity with Great Britain and how to accommodate out-of-country candidates. In both cases, the advice of the Council's solicitor, Francis H. Chrysler, was sought. There had been a thought that the reciprocity question could be moved forward if the Medical Council could consider a British registration sufficient to allow registration in the Canada Medical Register without examination. Chrysler advised that "no such provision appeared in the Act." His opinion on the other matter basically gave the same rationale. According to the Act, holders of diplomas from outside of Canada must "approach this Council through the same channels" as Canadian medical graduates, by producing an enabling certificate or licence from one of the provinces.

July 1, 1913 was the next critical date for the Council. On that day the Canada Medical Register was opened, and the first entries made. The names of all members of the founding Council were inscribed without examination, as stipulated in the Canada Medical Act, with Roddick as the first entry, followed by Vice-President Thornton, and the remainder listed alphabetically. Powell was also voted the privilege of entry without examination "in consideration of services rendered prior to his actual engagement as Registrar," and a honourary registration, which was to be given only through unanimous vote, was created to recognize Roche. He had been a true friend to the Council in its early years, arguing for the Canada Medical Act as it was being debated in the House of Commons and working hard to secure funding for the Council.

The Council's "First Announcement" was also published that day. It described the examinations, which were a series of essay questions followed by a clinical oral examination. It also spelled out the rules that candidates must abide by during the examination and the fee schedule: $100 for the examination and registration,

---

The Council's first Registrar, Robert Henry Wynyard Powell was a long-time ally and confidant of Roddick's, and had worked closely with him to get the Canada Medical Act passed. Powell had been Sir John A. Macdonald's physician, President of the Canadian Medical Association in 1900 and instrumental in setting up the Canadian Medical Protective Association, as well as its first President, 1901-1934. He was Registrar until 1929, at which point ill health forced him to step down, but he remained Honourary Registrar until his death in 1935. Much of the early success in establishing the Medical Council of Canada can be credited to his foresight, tact and administrative ability.

and an additional $50 for those who required re-examination in cases of failure the first time round. A $100 fee was set for those falling under the "ten-year clause," which allowed anyone registered by a province ten years prior to November 7, 1912, the date upon which the Council was legally deemed to have come into operation, to be entered upon the Register without examination.

The first examinations were held October 7-10, 1913, at the McGill Medical Building and four Montreal hospitals: the General, Notre Dame, Royal Victoria and Hôtel-Dieu. They were a mix of essay questions and oral examinations in five broad topics covering public health and clinical subjects – a formula that was to remain virtually unchanged for over 50 years. The examinations were offered in both English and French, and required 28 examiners. Of the 71 candidates, 44 passed. In terms of cash flow, the examinations netted $7,100 for the Council's treasury. Expectations for the next round of examinations were bright, as by July 1914 Powell had almost 300 inquiries about them. There was, however, disappointment that only 85 doctors had applied for registration under the ten-year clause, as there had been high hopes that these licences would provide a welcome influx of cash.

The Medical Council of Canada was now well and truly launched, and, it was at this point, at the July 1, 1914 meeting, that Roddick asked permission to retire. As he summed it up, "I have lived for Dominion Registration now for more than twenty years and would like to be relieved of the responsibility in connection with the dear old lady, practically my sweetheart. Now that she has a bank account of her own, I think I can desert her without any remorse of conscience." No doubt his wife, the poet Amy Redpath Roddick, heartily supported this "separation." Roddick's wishes were respected, but he was voted Honourary President for life. Shortly after the Council meeting, Roddick received a knighthood for his lifetime of remarkable service and achievement.

Licentiate to Heal:
A History of the
Medical Council

At the Council's first meeting, a committee was struck to prepare the Council's official seal and diploma. After prolonged discussion, it was decided to adopt a design for the seal based on Harvey's Stemma and the term "Licentiate of the Medical Council of Canada" on the diploma, with the abbreviation LMCC for daily use after one's name.

5. GROWING PAINS

The long battle to establish the Medical Council of Canada had ended successfully, right on the doorstep of the First World War, which Canada entered on August 4, 1914. The impact was felt immediately. The war drained the country of its medical practitioners, as they were needed for active service. The urgency was so great that many candidates for Dominion registration had to forgo their examinations and proceed directly overseas. This created quite a dilemma for the Council. Throughout the war they were flooded with petitions, from all levels and from all over the country, about creating a special registration without examination to cover this situation. After some real soul searching and seeking of legal opinions, the Council decided that no such dispensation could be made, as it would contravene the Canada Medical Act.

As well, many of the examiners appointed for the June 1915 examinations in Winnipeg had been called up, requiring last minute scurrying to find replacements, and this was to be a perennial problem throughout the war. Even closer to home, by 1916 three members of the Council were overseas, with one, Walter Bapty, who had been the youngest of the founding members at 29 years of age, severely wounded. Canada's medical schools barely had any teaching staff left, and by the war's end, a longer-term pinch was being felt – students who would have enrolled in medical school had been siphoned off by the war effort, either by enlistment or conscription, with many never to return. Even Roddick was touched by the war. He and his wife had travelled to Europe at the

The Council's second President, Robert Thornton, summed up the effect of the First World War as having "so profoundly disturbed the general current of our lives, both national and individual, and in various ways the work of the Council." Despite growing pains exacerbated by a world in turmoil because of the war, the Council was on a solid footing by the end of the 1920s. Shown here, the aftermath of the bombing of No. 7 Canadian General Hospital at Étaples, France, on May 19, 1918, which killed 53 people.

The Honourable Robert S. Thornton,
the Council's second president, 1914-1915.

end of July 1914 after receiving his knighthood in England. What was intended to be a relaxing taking of the waters at Contrexéville in France, turned out to be a very difficult escape, and this was especially hard on the 68-year-old Roddick, whose health was not good.

The war also had a devastating effect on government budgets. The Council was fortunate to receive its annual $15,000 grant up until 1916, at which point the Minister of Finance turned down the request for a $5,000 grant for 1917 citing heavy war expenditures and the fact that the Council was fairly flush, with $40,000 in its treasury. This was a matter of great concern over the next few years, as the Council had lost money on the early examinations, and its apparent wealth would only get them through a few years of operation. Indeed, by 1919 the Council had run up a deficit of $6,335 in expenditures over receipts, and it remained in the red, eating up its capital, until 1925, which brought the first surplus ever – and a tidy sum it was at $10,386

Throughout the war and into the early 1920s, the Council was extremely concerned with the low turnout for the examinations. The first examination in 1912 had 71 candidates and there were small but encouraging increases over the next two years. The war caused a relentless decline in the annual turnout, reaching its nadir in 1918, with a paltry 31 candidates. Equally unhappy for the Council's treasury was the fact that fewer than anticipated numbers were seeking registration without examination under the ten-year clause. Powell was especially worried that those working as examiners were not bothering to seek Dominion registration, even though he took great pains to "intimate the desirability of registration" when setting up the annual arrangements with them. The examiners' lack of interest in registration was thought to be particularly damning and indicative of a widespread ambivalence about being a licentiate of the Medical Council of Canada. As a result, publicity became a major agenda item in the early 1920s, and a special committee was struck to "investigate fully the best means to popularize the examination of the Medical Council." One particularly successful initiative involved sending every fourth and fifth year medical student in the country an information package, in French or English, about the Council and the value of a licentiate. Powell credited this with welcome increases in registration starting in 1921.

> "The first so-called "triple centre" examinations took place in June 1920 in Toronto, Winnipeg and Vancouver, with a further examination offered in Montreal in October."

The most positive boost to the Council's credibility came from British Columbia's stunning decision in 1919 to eliminate its own provincial examination in favour of the Medical Council's, with the rider that examinations be offered in Vancouver each year. The Council had expanded its examinations to two sites a year starting in 1915, and the deal with British Columbia meant further expansion. The first so-called "triple centre" examinations took place in June 1920 in Toronto, Winnipeg and Vancouver, with a further examination offered in Montreal in October. The Council quickly embarked upon negotiations with other provinces, notably Alberta and New Brunswick, to set up similar arrangements, but these came to nothing.

All throughout the 1920s, reciprocity, especially with Great Britain, remained the Holy Grail that was always just beyond grasp. From its earliest meetings, the Council had devoted much time and effort to this thoroughly intractable problem. A special committee was set up, discussions took place at almost every meeting, Powell and others kept up an unwavering correspondence on the topic, and the Council even sent a delegation to Glasgow to meet with the President of the British Medical Council. It was a major concern as many considered the absence of reciprocity to be the single biggest detractor from the value of a licentiate. The solution to the matter was mired in complexity of the most opaque variety, requiring no less than that every province in Canada have its own reciprocity agreement in place with Great Britain followed by an amendment to the Canada Medical Act, which would, of course, require approval from each province, and then finetuning of Great Britain's own medical legislation.

These issues of profile, place in the world, and finances were all part and parcel of the growing pains to be expected for a new organization. By the end of the 1920s, though, the outlook for the Council was starting to look very bright. Once the troops were demobilized and life returned to peacetime routines, medical schools quickly got up and running, and the number of candidates

Licentiate to Heal: A History of the Medical Council of Canada

*The General Strike, which paralyzed Winnipeg from May 15 to June 25, 1919, was the cause
of a rare cancellation of a Council examination, which had been scheduled in that city for June 3.
Thornton was in the thick of it as a Minister in the Manitoba government and had to miss the 1919
Council meeting, which started on June 17.*

lining up for the Council's examination started to climb. Toward the end of the 1920s, appreciation of the value of a licentiate was widespread, with the majority of Canadian medical students signing up for the examination, as a matter of course, upon graduation. Surprisingly, the number of doctors applying under the ten-year clause increased post-war and continued at a reasonable pace throughout the 1920s, despite the original prediction that this option would run its course by about 1922. And much to Powell's delight, even the examiners started applying for their licentiate. By 1929, business was booming, with examinations running in eight centres across Canada and an incredible 372 candidates! The Council's budget was happily in the black after so many lean years, and it was able to rely solely on examination fees and solid investment decisions to support its operating costs.

There had been other major changes in the decade since the war's end. In 1918, Roddick missed an annual meeting for the first time, owing to his deteriorating health, and he was not to return. He died on February 20, 1923. At the 1923 annual meeting, his long-time friend Powell said, "Words quite fail me when I must officially report to you the death of Sir Thomas Roddick, the father of this Council and a man greatly beloved."

Powell, himself, continued on as the much admired, efficient and affable Registrar until 1929, when ill health came knocking at his door. Another Ottawa-based doctor and a friend of Powell's, John Fenton Argue took over the position on a temporary basis, but it soon became clear that Powell would have to step down and Argue became the Council's second Registrar. The last name Powell entered into the Canada Medical Register was LMCC No. 2301, a Joseph Kaufmann of Montreal under the ten-year clause, and one can only hope that he was an examiner who had finally seen the light. Powell was named Honourary Registrar with a generous annual stipend, which he received up until his death on April 4, 1935.

The Honourable W.J. Roche was an influential friend of the Medical Council in its early years. He spoke in support of the Canada Medical Act as it was being debated in the House of Commons; as Minister of the Interior, on behalf of the government, he officially opened the first meeting in 1912; and he worked hard, behind the scenes, to secure funding for the Council. In recognition, the Council unanimously voted Roche the first and only honourary registration ever granted, which saw his name inscribed in the Canada Medical Register on June 20, 1914. In 1919, he became a member of Council, representing the University of Western Ontario, of which he was then Chancellor.

Amy Redpath Roddick, as a tribute to her late husband, had a monumental main entrance erected at McGill. The Roddick Memorial Gates were officially opened on May 28, 1925 and shortly thereafter became an integral part of the convocation tradition at McGill.

6. CHANGING
of the GUARD

The new Registrar, John Fenton Argue was a force to be reckoned with. His was a brash, abrupt character guided by a fierce and abounding loyalty to the ideals and operations of the Council. While he would heap scorn of the most blistering magnitude on any young doctor foolish enough to have misplaced his or her valuable licentiate documents, he also made a special point in his annual report to Council to praise the attributes and contribution of any members lost to death or retirement.

With the new Registrar came the Council's first real office and regular secretarial staff. Powell, despite several attempts by Council to the contrary, had steadfastly maintained the Registrar's office at his home on Cooper Street and conducted most of the business single-handedly. This, however, was no longer feasible given the burgeoning workload caused by the steady increase in the number of candidates wishing to take the Council examinations. Indeed, in 1930, the year after Argue took on the position, the great majority of Canada's graduating medical students (299 out of 350) signed up for the examination. The new office was located a few blocks from Parliament Hill in the Medical Arts Building at 180 Metcalfe Street.

Argue's appointment was made at the Council meeting of September 4, 1929, a mere month before the stock market crash that triggered a decade-long, global depression. Canada was particularly hard hit, given a persistent drought in the Prairies that devastated vital wheat crops. At the Depression's height in 1933, Canada's unemployment rate hit 27% and the gross national product was down by 43%. The Depression had no ill effect whatsoever on the Council. Quite the contrary, in fact! With an ever-expanding list of fee-paying candidates and the general decrease in cost of living, the Council doubled its treasury during the Depression years. When the Second World War was declared on September 10, 1939, the Council had about $115,000 in its coffers, most of which was safely invested in long-term bonds. This prosperity was achieved in spite of the fact that examination fees were reduced twice to lessen the financial burden on students: from $100 to $75 in 1932, and to $50 in 1941. By the late 1930s, a recurring issue on the agenda was a discussion of what useful endeavour the surplus should support, with ideas ranging from building a suitable headquarters to setting up scholarships for candidates with outstanding examination results.

Corporate memory was definitely not a problem for the Council during this period. Edward M. Morgan, a homeopathic representative, was the last of the founding members to serve as President (1935-1936). He retired from Council in 1942, after 30 years of service. The Council's second President, Robert S. Thornton (1914-1915), who had been such a friend and ally of Roddick's in setting up the Council, died on September 18, 1936, and he had been an active member until 1934. The last of the founders to leave the table was Walter W. White in 1946; he had represented the College of Physicians and Surgeons of New Brunswick for 34 years and was the Council's fourth President (1916-1917).

John Fenton Argue, the Council's second Registrar, was a well-known Ottawa personality who was deeply committed to the medical profession and had a remarkable record of service. He ran his practice, which he established in 1897, for more than 50 years, and was also the Medical Health Officer for Gloucester Township, 1898-1946, and the County of Carleton gaol surgeon, 1900-1946. He held numerous executive positions in professional associations, including President of the Ottawa Medico-Chirurgical Society, the Council of Physicians and Surgeons of Ontario, and the Canadian Medical Protective Association, which he helped Robert Powell found. He was Registrar for almost a quarter century, from June 1929 to December 1954, at which point he reluctantly retired at the age of 83. He died July 16, 1956, and his funeral was attended by a who's who of the medical profession, as well as Ottawa's colourful Mayor Charlotte Whitton.

While new technologies such as this "snow plane" were making it easier for the busy country doctor to get to his patients, the specialization of medicine, which was on the rise in the 1930s, was making serious inroads into the professional stature of the general practitioner. Shown here, John Card (LMCC No. 4931), father of Robert Card (LMCC No. 24815) and grandfather of Sharon Card (LMCC No. 72029) in Ayton, Ontario, 1940.

Conjoint examinations became a reality in 1940 primarily because of Stanley Ryerson's 13-year campaign of lobbying the Medical Council and the universities. Ryerson came by his persistence and tireless energy naturally, as he was a descendent of the formidable Egerton Ryerson who had set up Ontario's first-rate primary and secondary school system in the early 1870s after a 27-year effort. Ryerson served on the Council until 1944.

As the old guard changed, there were some real movers and shakers joining the Council, and foremost amongst them was E. Stanley Ryerson, who became the University of Toronto's representative in 1932. It was due to his efforts that the concept of conjoint examinations became a reality after 13 long years of lobbying on his part. He had first appeared before the Council to promote the idea in 1927, as the convenor of a delegation from the Canadian Medical Association. This eminently logical proposal was to be a boon to the poor medical student in that it meant the writing of only one examination to obtain both a degree and licentiate. One of Ryerson's first actions as a Council member was to table a detailed proposal outlining the procedures and division of responsibilities for conjoint examinations. In a nutshell, the Council's Main Board of Examiners would set the examination as in the past, but both the university and the Council would appoint the examiners. The university would consider the marks given for the written, clinical and oral examinations for granting the student's degree, and then all examination results of successful students would be passed along to the Medical Council for consideration of the licentiate.

Acceptance of the idea was slow in building, as is natural where change requires a sharing of powers, but Ryerson was strongly supported in his efforts by many Council members, notably the University of Manitoba representative, A.T. Mathers. Finally, in 1940, it was approved, and the following year 271 students took conjoint examinations at four of the nine Canadian medical schools: Manitoba, Queen's, Toronto and Western Ontario. It must have been icing on the cake, indeed, for Ryerson to sit as the Council's President (1940-1941), the year of those first conjoint examinations.

One important emerging issue that the energetic Ryerson tackled, but with absolutely no success, was in lobbying, in 1933, for the Council to take responsibility for national qualifications for specialist practice. There was only lukewarm support for this proposal, and Argue was tasked with testing the waters with the provincial boards, seeing as acceptance of Ryerson's proposal would require an amendment to the Canada Medical Act, which each of the provinces would have to approve. Nothing much was accomplished on this front, and when Ryerson read his final report at the 1936 meeting, there was no follow up or even any discussion. Ryerson continued his interest in the file and was involved in its successful resolution in 1937, when the Royal College of Physicians and Surgeons of Canada took on the responsibility.

There was, however, very encouraging movement on streamlining provincial licences and the national licentiate, with the decisions by Ontario in 1934 and New Brunswick in 1939 to forego their own examinations in favour of the Council's. These were huge steps toward the long-held dream of making the Medical Council "the sole portal" for medical practitioners registering in any province. There was less positive movement on the question of uniformity of provincial enabling certificates, which candidates required in order to take the Council examinations. Each province had different requirements, and there were concerns that some were too lenient and others too restrictive. A meeting of all provincial registrars in 1932, encouraged by the Council, resulted in little more than an exchange of information about the various diverse standards and polite mutterings of how helpful that had been. This was a matter, however, that would not be going away anytime soon, as it was inextricably bound to the issue of assuring the competence of graduates of foreign medical schools seeking credentials to practise in Canada.

The Medical Council's first real office was located at 180 Metcalfe Street in downtown Ottawa. Following Powell's retirement in 1929, Argue rented space in the brand new Art Deco-style Medical Arts Building, which was designed by Werner Ernst Noffke, one of Ottawa's most influential and prolific architects.

Chapter

7. WAR *and* POST-WAR MEASURES

The Second World War started just days after the 1939 meeting, and it had an immediate but very different impact on the Council than the previous war. The damage caused by the hasty mobilization of most of the country's medical infrastructure for the First World War had taught everyone a big lesson. The Medical Council promptly sent an advisory to the government warning against a similar wholesale enlistment of medical students, and most of Canada's medical schools went into overdrive with accelerated courses. And this is where the war was to affect the Council the most.

The accelerated schedule meant that universities could graduate a new group of doctors every eight months instead of every twelve, creating a much larger number of candidates for the licentiate. As a result, the Registrar's Office and the Main Board of Examiners carried a crushing workload throughout the war. The Council's examination schedule, which since 1915 had included one spring exam in May or June and one fall exam in October, had to be thrown out the window so that graduates of the accelerated course could get their licentiate prior to their internship, which had been shortened as well to eight months. The numbers were staggering. In 1943, a particularly bumper year, 763 candidates took the Council exam, which was offered in January, July and October. To put that into context, pre-war candidates were about half that number.

Fortunately for the overburdened Argue, on September 8, 1942, he hired Alice Wilcox, a veritable whirlwind of efficiency and good humour. She had heard about the stenographer's job through her close friends, Argue's son and daughter-in-law, and had jumped at the opportunity because her previous position at the Passport Office offered little room for learning or advancement. Even with his load lightened by the able new assistant, Argue, who was by then in his 70s, frequently yearned for a return to the simpler examination schedule. His wish was partially granted post-war when the spring and fall schedule was reinstated, but the examinations continued to be held in many more locations across Canada on a complicated schedule owing to the conjoint format, and the number of candidates kept climbing. By 1953, a thousand plus became the annual norm. The Main Board of Examiners faced an equally huge challenge. The spring schedule required that they prepare three different but comparable examinations to accommodate the requirements of the medical schools. There were repeated conversations with the universities about coordinating their schedules so only two examinations would be needed, but this proved impossible to resolve.

A.T. Mathers, who had been such an ally of Ryerson's on the issue of conjoint examinations, was an influential innovator in the 1940s. At the 1942 meeting, at which he presided as President, Mathers, citing the value of the Association of American Medical Colleges, urged the university representatives on the Council to organize themselves into a similar group and hold their own meeting, aligned to the dates of the Council's which they all attended, so as to provide a forum to discuss medical education issues and experiments in medical pedagogy. This was met with wholehearted support. In a tag team move, it was Ryerson, along with the McGill representative, J.F. McIntosh, who officially tabled the recommendation that steps be instituted to establish an Association of Canadian Medical Colleges, and that they hold its first meeting linked to the Council's next meeting. And they did precisely that the following August 31, the day preceding the Council's 1943 meeting. The organization has continued to this day, changing its name to the Association of Faculties of Medicine of Canada in 2004.

"The Government should appreciate the fact that the turning out of doctors for war purposes is just as much a war industry as the manufacture of planes and tanks." Stanley Ryerson, President (1940-41). Shown here, the No. 5 Field Surgical Unit in training at No. 10 Canadian General Hospital, a 1200-bed field hospital in Normandy and Belgium during the Second World War, most of whose medical personnel were professors or graduates of the University of Western Ontario.

Alice Wilcox, who was a loyal and indispensable employee for 35 years, left some colourful vignettes about work at the Council. In the early 1950s, she recounts, the Medical Register was updated twice a year. This meant signing up to 500 diplomas at a shot, a particularly tedious job, but one for which Argue had worked out a system. They would take the diplomas to his house, which had a large living room table, and he would sit at one end signing. Because he did not permit the use of blotting paper, Wilcox had to take each diploma as it was signed, dash to the end of the room, place it on the floor to dry, then rush back for the next one. Argue used a stopwatch to see how many he could sign in a minute, and sometimes he signed faster than she could run. One day when the job was finished and the floor covered with drying diplomas, Argue stood up and tripped over a lamp cord. This sent a heavy Tiffany lamp flying and it hit the inkbottle, which sailed through the air and crashed into a wall. India ink poured down the wall ruining the diplomas, not to mention Argue's wallpaper and carpet. One can imagine that life with Argue at the helm was never dull.

Licentiate to Heal:
A History of the
Medical Council
of Canada

Despite an impressive track record of achievements that had broadened the influence and solidified the reputation of the Medical Council, there were many on Council in the 1940s who were growing concerned about its increasing complacency and inflexible routine. Granted the Council was constrained by the rigid statutes of the Canada Medical Act, but the annual meeting now followed a structure basically unchanged since 1912, and much of that was rote rather than substance. Most worrisome was a marked tendency for pressing issues raised at one year's meeting never to be addressed again or to be sent off to a special committee whose report the next year re-assigned the issue to the provinces or universities. Part of the blame for this creeping superficiality was attributed to the fact that in 1924 the annual meeting had been trimmed back to a one-day event as a cost-cutting measure. In 1949, with the specific goal of providing more time for discussion of matters of policy, the two-day meeting format was reinstated.

This rejuvenated the work of the Council, and just in time because some earth-shattering issues were pushing their way into the Council's deliberations. Specialization was rapidly changing the face of medicine in Canada and seriously eroding the professional stature of general practitioners, resulting in the establishment of the College of General Practice (now Family Physicians) of Canada in 1954. Of particular concern to the Council, specialization was creating persistent pressure for new examination areas, and by 1953 a special committee was struck to look at the appropriate mix of subjects that should be covered on the Council's examination. The movement toward some form of universal, government-funded health insurance was also gaining momentum, and every medical group in the country was mobilizing in opposition. While not of direct bearing to the daily operations of the Council, it was a topic frequently debated in terms of the impact it would have on the overall fabric and functioning of the medical community.

"The Council by the mid-1950s had increased to
38 members, with the addition of representatives for the
universities of Alberta (1925), Ottawa (1946), British
Columbia (1951) and Saskatchewan (1954), plus two
representatives for the Newfoundland Medical Board."

The Council also made a decision in 1952 that would fundamentally alter the
timing of its examination, and this was a very controversial one, proposed
during a long overdue overhaul of the Council's regulations. It took almost
three years of debate and consensus building for all the provinces to agree that
a compulsory one-year internship should be an additional basic requirement
toward receiving the licentiate of the Medical Council, but agree they did.
Fortunately this change was safely within the powers of the Executive to make
through an Order-in-Council, and no amendment to the Canada Medical Act
was required. It cannot be stressed too much how constricting the clauses of the
Act had been to the Medical Council. Time after time, new activities had been
suggested, ranging from scholarships to comparative studies of medical schools,
only to be shelved on the advice of legal counsel that the Act made no provision
for such an initiative. Even the oft-debated question of a suitable headquarters
for the Council was constrained by the Act, which stipulated a cap of $25,000
for any real estate holdings – an amount that would have been reasonable when
the clause was written, but laughable for the mid-1950s.

The growing irrelevancy of words cast in legislative stone in 1911 to the needs
of the medical profession in Canada in the mid-twentieth century was an
ever-increasing source of friction. The dangers of attempting an overhaul of
the Act, however, were daunting in the extreme. The process would require the
amending bill to pass through both the Senate and House of Commons, if a
sympathetic member of each house could be found to table it. Worse, there was
no guarantee that the process would end in the result desired by the Council,
as both levels could suggest their own amendments to the bill. Not to mention
that if and when it squeaked through at the federal level, each of the provinces

would then have to pass enabling legislation. Understandably this was deemed so overwhelming a prospect that the Council continued to work within the Act's confines – for the time being.

Membership on the Council grew when Newfoundland joined Canada in 1949. The 1912 Council had had 32 members, but it had expanded over the years with the opening of new medical schools, which each rated a representative at the table. The Council by the mid-1950s had increased to 38 members, with the addition of representatives for the universities of Alberta (1925), Ottawa (1946), British Columbia (1951) and Saskatchewan (1954), plus two representatives for the Newfoundland Medical Board. One of them, Cluny Macpherson, became the Council's second Newfoundland-born President in 1954-1955, the first, of course, having been Sir Thomas Roddick. Macpherson, interestingly, had been an admiring student of Roddick's just as he was working to push the Canada Medical Act through.

In counterpoint to these additions to the Council, there was one important departure. John Fenton Argue retired at the end of 1954, after an impressive quarter century of service and at the ripe age of 83. At about the same time, Volume No. 1 of the Canada Medical Register was also retired. Used from July 1, 1913 to June 29, 1953, the Register is a massive leather-bound book inscribed with the names of 14,099 licentiates, each entry handwritten by the Registrar. As one of his last acts, Argue sought and was granted permission to go to a loose-leaf format for Volume No. 2 of the Register, thus enabling the typing in of the licentiate names.

The first volume of the Canada Medical Register is a priceless artifact for Canada's medical community. Covering a 40-year period from July 1, 1913 to June 29, 1953, it records the names of the Council's first 14,099 licentiates. In its ink-splotched pages there is one truly perplexing mystery. The founding Council members are the first 32 entries, but curiously the sixteenth line, which should have held A.W.H. Lindsay's name, was left blank. This was the same Lindsay who had been so helpful as the unpaid co-interim Registrar and who had been active on many Council committees. Lindsay died in 1915, and his contribution to the Council was lauded in the minutes of the 1916 meeting. There is no hint to be found of the reason for his omission from the Register.

Licentiate to Heal:
A History of the
Medical Council
of Canada

A.W.H. Lindsay

8. EXAMINATION TRANSFORMED

Hugh Stephen became the Council's third Registrar on January 1, 1955, after serving a three-month probationary term under Argue. Recently retired from the Royal Canadian Army Medical Corps where he had gained a strong background in administration, the quiet, unobtrusive Stephen was a marked contrast in personality to that of his flamboyant predecessor. By year-end, the Medical Council had moved to the new Commonwealth Building at 77 Metcalfe Street, which was two blocks closer to Parliament Hill and is now the site of a modern office complex.

Stephen and Alice Wilcox were an efficient team, and the examinations, scattered throughout the country on a complicated schedule, ran like precision clockwork. With the new office, came all new office furniture and the latest equipment required by the "dictates of efficient business administration." Stephen was a master of the fine detail, and in 1956 he introduced a new style of reporting examination results that received commendation all round. His statistical analyses of the annual candidates' results provided a meticulous comparison, broken down by university and by country, to all previous results from 1919 to 1956 – startling documents by today's standards of confidentiality. Another of his well-received innovations was the verbatim recording of the meetings, for which he employed Hansard-trained reporters – George Baker, who took on the task in 1959, was a fixture at Council meetings up until 1988, and shortly thereafter audio recording took over.

Medicine was evolving rapidly, and this was reflected in changes to the Board of Examiners for 1960 when examiners in pediatrics were appointed for the first time and in homeopathy for the last time. There had been mounting pressure to add pediatrics on the grounds that it accounted for about a third of the practice of general medicine in Canada. On the flip side of the coin, homeopathy had fallen into an almost total decline – a marked contrast to its position at the turn of the twentieth century, when its practitioners had sufficient clout to hold up the passing of the Canada Medical Act by a full year following their successful lobbying for inclusion in the Medical Council. They had supplied the three homeopathic members specified by the Act until 1945, when only two could be found. The resignation of C.W. Becker in 1959 after 34 years of service left only J. J. Griffith, up until his death in 1968.

Finances became a problem during the 1960s, as the Council had started running at a deficit in 1959, and it was forced to dip into its capital for the first time since 1924. Rising operating costs and a slump in the market value of the Council's investments were the culprits. By 1965, Stephen was warning that current savings were about enough to cover the expenses of a single year. Gradual increases in the examination fee from $125 in 1959 to $175 in 1966 reversed this worrisome trend.

A major transformation of all aspects of the medical profession was triggered by the Royal Commission on Health Services, chaired by Justice Emmett M. Hall. One of its findings rang alarm bells about a projected shortfall in medical practitioners, and this was to have a huge impact on the Council. The response was to open more medical schools and to encourage more foreign-trained doctors to move to Canada. There were serious concerns about how the Council would be able to accommodate such a dramatic increase in demand for its examinations.

Even before the Hall Commission reports were published in 1964, the Council had been worried about the logistical challenges of assessing what were already large numbers of candidates. Marking the essay-style questions and conducting meaningful clinical orals were becoming overwhelming tasks. Worse, there were concerns about the accuracy and fairness of the results, as the adequacy of the range of knowledge sampled by the written exam was being increasingly questioned, and there were great discrepancies in the marks not only from centre to centre but also from examiner to examiner. Everyone realized that these could not be corrected simply by a modification of the existing system.

Hugh Montrose Stephen, the Council's third Registrar, continued the tradition of longevity of service set by Powell and Argue, and worked past retirement age at the Council's request. During his 16 years as Registrar he helped the Council in its first major overhaul of its examinations in 50 years, resulting in a complete transformation that replaced the traditional essay and oral exams with objective, computer-marked, multiple-choice questions. He also saw the membership of the Council grow with the addition of representatives for each of the four medical schools spawned by the Hall Commission's recommendations: Sherbrooke joined in 1968, and Calgary, McMaster and Memorial in 1971.

To celebrate its 50th anniversary, the Council contributed to the Royal College's new archives room, so that it could be set up in honour of the Medical Council's founder, Sir Thomas Roddick. The entire Council attended the dedication of the Roddick Room on September 10, 1962. D. Sclater Lewis, the Royal College's archivist and past Chair of the Main Board of Examiners and Cluny Macpherson, a past President of the Council and a student of Roddick's, are shown at the opening in front of Roddick's portrait.

By 1962, the Council had already set up a special committee, chaired by Donald F. Cameron, to look at more efficient and trustworthy methods of assessment. As this was a profession-wide concern, representatives of the Canadian Medical Association, the Royal College of Physicians and Surgeons of Canada and the College of General Practice of Canada took part in the discussions. Advice and assistance were sought from the National Board of Medical Examiners as they were pioneering new testing techniques in the United States. By 1965, the Council had approved in principle the "progressive introduction of objective, machine-marked examinations to supplement or replace the present essay-type written examinations and of programmed, erasure or similar examinations to supplement or replace the present clinical and oral examinations."

This was a momentous decision indeed, representing the first major reform of the Council's examinations since 1912. Events unfolded quickly, and in 1967 the Council ran a successful test examination in one of its five topics, "Medicine, including Therapeutics," and the following year, the multiple-choice format was used exclusively in place of the essay questions. In 1970 the new format, using answer by erasure to uncover information or results of actions, was implemented to replace the oral clinical examination, and psychiatry, long-lobbied for, was added to the list of test subjects.

In less than a decade, the Council had completely revamped its examination formula, which had been virtually unchanged for 50 years. An important offshoot of the exercise was that it fostered a new spirit of collaboration with other professional associations involved in questions of medical education and qualifications. Their representatives started attending the Council meetings regularly as observers, and the Council theirs. Another benefit was the streamlining effect on the examination schedule, as the new format exams lent themselves to being run on the same days for everyone. From May 6-8, 1970, the Council ran its first single examination session since 1913, with candidates doing the French version in three cities and the English in eleven. Almost 2,000 candidates took the new exam, and more than half were from outside Canada.

The Main Board of Examiners also had a major change in its job description. The computer-marked questions were either right or wrong, so there was no longer a need for reviewing controversial examination results, which had been a large part of its duties. Setting the examination questions was transformed radically, but was not made any less time-consuming. Through its subject test committees, the Main Board now assisted in selecting questions from the vast collection maintained by the National Board of Medical Examiners, which then put together the examination papers, in both French and English, and delivered them to the examination centres. Granted there was now a large fee to be paid to the National Board of Medical Examiners, but this was more than counterbalanced by the dramatic drop in costs to support the numerous examiners required by the old system. Plus, as forecast, there was an equally dramatic increase in candidates lining up to take the examinations. The Council entered the 1970s with a whole new approach to its examinations, and its books happily back in the black.

In the fall of 1969, the Medical Council moved from its downtown office to the new headquarters of the Canadian Medical Association, located in the heart of a growing suburban community in Ottawa's east end. As Hugh Stephen described it, CMA House, at 1867 Alta Vista Drive, offered more dignified and commodious space, parking for visitors and closer connections with the Canadian Medical Association. The annual meeting was held there in 1970 for the first and last time, as Council members preferred the convenience, acoustics and catering of their traditional downtown meeting place, the Château Laurier.

9. THE REVOLUTION SPREADS

The search for a new Registrar began in 1970, when Hugh Stephen was 67. Powell and Argue had worked well into their seventies and eighties, respectively; but times had changed, and 65 was now fully entrenched as the standard retirement age. Roger Rouleau became the Council's fourth Registrar on January 1, 1972, following a five-month probationary period working with Stephen to learn the ropes. The 52-year-old Rouleau was personable and a superb administrator, and he quickly became well liked and admired by the office staff and Council members. Shortly after his appointment, however, illness struck, and he was off work for an extended period. He returned to work in April 1973, but, tragically, died on July 28. Desmond Magner, the University of Ottawa's representative on Council who had been a member of the selection committee for Rouleau, filled in as interim Registrar, but, in a sad coincidence, he too died unexpectedly, at the young age of 60, just days after John Barr became the fifth Registrar on November 15, 1973. During this period of intense upheaval, it was the steady hand of Alice Wilcox that kept the Council going, with no discernible interruption in operations.

Barr came from the military, and despite a steep learning curve in his early days with the Council, he quickly settled in. His gracious, good-humoured nature made an immediate positive impression on everyone at the Council, but it was his masterful grasp of complex issues and the complicated examination process that made him worth his weight in gold. A self-deprecating man, he joked that any success he achieved in administering the Council was because much of his army career had been spent finding inventive ways to get round the administrators.

The total overhaul of its examinations had given the Council a taste for change, and another radical departure from the past took place in 1976, this time involving the venerable Canada Medical Act – and at a breathtaking pace. In January, a small sub-committee, led by the current President J.C.C. Dawson, met to look at revisions to the Act that would enable the Council to broaden the scope of its activities. Amending the Act was a daunting, time-consuming process – and fraught with danger, as undesired changes, completely out of the Council's control, could be added during the legislation's journey through the Senate and House of Commons. So, despite the fact that the Act had "cribbed and confined" the Council's operations in many ways since 1912, there had never been the will or overwhelming need to amend it. It was now absolutely essential, as the Medical Council had set new objectives that included working cooperatively with other groups in Canada and abroad involved in the licensure and assessment of medical students and practitioners, and conducting research and development in those realms – none of which was permitted by the Act.

Charles Scott, their solicitor, recommended as an alternate route that the Council apply for Letters Patent of Continuance, a fairly recent option that allowed corporations to take themselves out from under the direct control of Parliament. This met with unanimous support, and with the blessing of the entire Executive Committee, a draft application was presented at the September 1976 Council meeting, where it was approved with very little discussion. Within a matter of days, on September 22, 1976, the Minister of Consumer and Corporate Affairs issued the Letters Patent. This was a truly major breakthrough.

Roger Lorenzo Lucien Joseph Rouleau, the fourth Registrar and its first French one, was born in Ottawa and a graduate of Laval. He brought to the job 20 years of experience as a general practitioner in rural eastern Ontario and in the Ottawa area, where he also was the Medical Officer of Health for what is now Vanier and coroner for the County of Carleton, as well as holding positions at the University of Ottawa and Ottawa General Hospital. His expertise in medical administration earned him a consultant's position with the federal department of National Health and Welfare in 1967, where he worked until his appointment with the Council. His tenure as Registrar was tragically cut short by his death by drowning during a fishing trip on the St. Lawrence.

Something that had been long discussed, but never before attempted, had been achieved in less than a year. The Medical Council was now empowered to implement its new programs, and should the future bring the need for further revision of the By-Laws that now governed them, this was a simple process. Amendments required a 12-month advance notification, an affirmative vote of two thirds of the Council members, then approval by the Minister of Consumer and Corporate Affairs.

Another major change was the repatriation of the examinations from the National Board of Medical Examiners. The multiple-choice format had been a huge success, but there were growing concerns about the lack of Canadian content, plus some worrisome logistics issues. For example, a strike of airport workers in 1974 paralyzed airfreight services between the U.S. and Canada just as the three-tonne shipment of examinations was due to leave Philadelphia for distribution to 16 examination centres across Canada. The examination papers arrived at the last possible moment. If they had not, the Council would probably have had to refund the fees and any related travel expenses of its 2,800 registered candidates.

The candidate-in-waiting was the R.S. McLaughlin Examination and Research Centre, which the Royal College had established as a Canadian equivalent of the National Board. The Centre, which opened officially on July 1, 1969 with offices at both the University of Alberta and Laval, was funded through a $250,000 grant from the R. Samuel McLaughlin Foundation. McLaughlin was one of Canada's most generous philanthropists, and he set up his foundation in 1951, in part, to help counteract the exodus of young doctors from Canada by providing grants and fellowships that would encourage them to stay. By the time it ceased operation in 2001, the foundation had donated nearly $200 million to various causes, much of which benefited the medical profession.

John Wilmer Browning Barr, the fifth Registrar, like Hugh Stephen, came from the Canadian Armed Forces where he had a distinguished career culminating in his appointment, in 1970, as Surgeon-General. He tackled the job of Registrar like a military operation, briefing himself so thoroughly that within months of his appointment in November 1973, he authored an acclaimed nine-part series about the history and operations of the Council for the CMA Journal. During his nine years with the Council, he was a key player in developing the Letters Patent that allowed the Council to transform itself to meet modern demands. A deep respect for tradition spurred his initiative to commission a Coat of Arms for the Council. Indeed, upon his retirement in December 1981, the one duty he continued was that of Colonel Commandant of the Forces' medical branch — an honourary post that involved reporting quarterly to Her Majesty Queen Elizabeth the Queen Mother, who was Colonel-in-Chief of the medical services.

The Medical Council was keenly interested and involved in the Centre's development, and supported it through annual donations from as early as 1968. Connections with the Royal College became much closer as a result, and key figures in the McLaughlin Centre's development, such as Robert B. Kerr and Donald R. Wilson, had a foot in each camp. Kerr, who had been back-to-back President of the Royal College (1966-1968) and the Council (1968-1969), was a strong proponent of the Centre and played a critical liaison role. Wilson, who became the McLaughlin Centre's first director, had been the Council's consultant on examinations since 1967, providing valuable input during the change to the multiple-choice format, and remained so until 1977. By 1975, the McLaughlin Centre had been tasked with producing a "made in Canada" examination for the subject area, "Public Health and Preventive Medicine", and so began the gradual transfer of responsibility from the National Board of Medical Examiners. The repatriation was completed on a five-year plan, and 2,557 candidates took the first all-Canadian multiple-choice examination in May 1980. As another first, the two-part examination had been streamlined into a single, comprehensive format.

There was another important development on the examinations front at this time: the institution of an evaluating examination to test the competence of graduates of foreign medical schools wishing to practise in Canada. This issue had popped up on the agenda many times over the years, but had never been resolved. Legalities hinging upon the Council's right to give the examination without enabling certificates from the provinces had always tied the discussion up in knots. The Canada Medical Act seemed clearly to say yes, but not all the provinces agreed. Legal opinions were lined up on each side of the argument, resulting in total inertia at the end of each bout. Further difficulties arose from the great variance in qualifications required by the different provinces in granting their certificates – another much-discussed matter, whose resolution was years away.

Alice Wilcox, who was given the title Assistant Registrar in 1973, retired in 1977. During her long career with the Medical Council, a standard feature of annual meetings was a tribute to her competence and good nature. Between September 8, 1942 and September 30, 1977, she worked for four widely disparate Registrars, served 37 Presidents, and had a hand in the inscription of 37,019 names into the Canada Medical Register. Suzanne Faulds became the new Assistant Registrar.

Increased immigration of physicians to Canada starting in the late 1960s and a request from the federal government, however, forced the question one more time. By 1977 it was finally resolved, supported by a variety of medical associations, most notably the Federation of Provincial Medical Licensing Authorities of Canada, and with an offer from the Canada Employment and Immigration Commission to assist in the administration of examinations abroad. The bottom line was that foreign graduates had to write the Council's evaluating examination in order to receive an enabling certificate from the provinces, which would then allow them to write the Council's qualifying examinations required by the provinces to issue a licence to practise. The McLaughlin Centre developed the examination, and the first one was offered, on a trial basis, in January 1979 at four locations in Canada and five abroad. Only 25 candidates took the exam, but these modest numbers exploded the next year to over 400, and continued to grow.

The development of the evaluating examination had very much been a group effort, and one important offshoot was closer cooperation with the Federation of Provincial Medical Licensing Authorities. This was formalized and strengthened further in 1979 when the Federation set up its secretariat at the Council office in Ottawa. Another more subtle shift was happening at the Council table itself. In 1977, Elizabeth S. Hillman became the Council's first woman member, a Governor-in-Council appointee from St. John's, and during her time on Council she lobbied relentlessly for student representation at the table. Fittingly, Hillman, who became the Council's first woman President (1981-1982), had been welcomed to the Council by its first Acadian President, Philippe d'Entremont (1976-1977). The baby boomers, too, were starting to put in an appearance.

The 1970s had been a decade of staggering change for the Council. There had been three Registrars, the qualifying examination had been repatriated and streamlined, the new evaluating examination launched, and, most important for its continuing evolution, the Council now had the authority, through its new Letters Patent, to direct its future path.

Chapter

10. MORE WORK *and* NEW DIMENSIONS

Entering the 1980s, the Council was carrying a workload of crushing proportions. The long-term effects of the Hall Commission had kicked in by the mid-1970s, and Canada's medical schools started producing bumper crops of graduates. Indeed, in 1976, the Council had its largest number of candidates for the qualifying examination ever, with 1,655 of the 3,004 being new graduates – well over double the numbers from the mid-1960s. There were also shifts in procedure brought about by the transfer of the examination to the McLaughlin Centre. Fortunately, the right people were in place. Thanks to John Barr's superlative administrative talents and his seasoned staff, as well as the Herculean efforts of the Examination Board and the test committees who worked with the McLaughlin Centre to set the questions, the examinations ran with surprisingly few hitches. And these were usually attributable to external events; for example, a two-month mail strike in July and August 1981 caused huge problems in corresponding with candidates for the September examination that year.

The evaluating examination had added a whole new dimension to the equation. By the mid-1980s the numbers of candidates applying to take the examination had skyrocketed into the stratosphere, with over 2,000 taking the examination at five centres in Canada and 20 overseas. Despite assistance from federal government employees in administering the examination, the bottom line was that all the paperwork had to funnel through the Council's small staff, and this required screening the applications, checking credentials, handling the finances,

and fielding questions from candidates, not to mention managing the logistics for the many examination centres. In March 1986, an unusually large number of candidates in Saudi Arabia required one of the Council's staff to travel to the Canadian embassy in Riyadh to help supervise the examination.

Barr retired at the end of 1981, although he was retained as a consultant and named Registrar Emeritus. Another recently retired Surgeon-General, Wilson Leach, became the Council's sixth Registrar, effective January 1, 1982, after a 14-month stint as Associate Registrar. In a curious coincidence, at the 1981 annual meeting where Leach's appointment as Registrar was announced, in addition to Barr, all three of the Council's future Registrars were present as members: Michel Bérard representing the Corporation Professionelle des médecins du Québec; Dale Dauphinee, McGill; and Ian Bowmer as the new representative of Memorial.

It was Leach who had to deal with the complicated logistics and fallout from the evaluating examination. The issue that was to cause him major headaches was the dramatic failure rate and the Council's policy to provide no feedback to candidates other than the pass or fail result. Leach was to spend much time responding to correspondence on this matter and, in many instances, dealing with the Human Rights Commission. Broad social changes were also having an impact on the way the Council was doing business. Throughout the 1980s there was a gradual switch of all the examination questions to the metric system, and increasing sensitivity to accessibility issues brought a new policy and procedures to accommodate disabled candidates writing the examinations. The Council's growing profile on the world stage resulted in its first international outreach case in 1982, when Council staff hosted the head of the Nigerian Medical Council for a seven-day training period. Nationally, other groups such as the pharmacists and dentists were looking at the Council as a model for their own qualifying examinations and policies.

Wilson George Leach became the sixth Registrar in 1982 and had a short but eventful five-year term. His main focus was the new evaluating examination, which added a significant layer of administrative complexity to the running of Council operations. His background mirrored that of John Barr's, in that each had retired from the Canadian Forces as Surgeon-General, with the rank of Major General. Leach's background was an interesting blend of administration and research. His development of a partial-pressure flight suit to protect aircrews from the effects of high altitudes earned him a place in Canada's Aviation Hall of Fame in 1974.

The R.S. McLaughlin Centre had been under contract since November 19, 1976 to develop the Council's examinations and carry out directed research on a wide range of questions linked to the validity, accuracy and the appropriateness of the examinations. The Council was its major external client, and linkages with the Centre were very close at all levels, from test committees to Council members and office staff. In the summer of 1987, the McLaughlin Centre relocated to Ottawa – an eminently sensible move given that its parent body, the Royal College, and the Medical Council were both based there. However, as early as the mid-1980s, there had been serious questions raised about the annual cost to the Council of purchasing the services of the McLaughlin Centre and the fact that the test questions, developed with the assistance of the Council's test committees, remained the property of the Centre.

Licentiate to Heal:
A History of the
Medical Council
of Canada

Accommodation was another major issue. The lease at CMA House was set to expire on December 31, 1984, and much uncertainty revolved around the question of relocation. As it turned out the discussion about a new home was shelved at the last moment, but only for a short time, with the offer from the Canadian Medical Association to extend the lease. The need for more space, though, and the desire for a home of its own, quickly brought it back onto the agenda. Part of the push to buy its own headquarters, in fact, was based on the desire at some point in the near future to take control of its examinations from the McLaughlin Centre, and to have space to accommodate this as an in-house function. After prolonged debate, the Council decided to take the plunge, and become a property owner for the first time in its history. On April 6, 1990, the Medical Council set up its headquarters on the third floor of a new office condominium in Ottawa's east end.

Leach had retired on January 31, 1987, owing to health problems. His replacement was Michel Bérard, who had joined the Council in 1978 and who stepped down from the presidency in order to become the seventh Registrar. Bérard's appointment was groundbreaking. It was the first time a Council member had become Registrar, and it represented the culmination of a long debate about the need for the Registrar to have experience at the Council table. Given the difficult issues that were facing the Council at this time, it was an excellent decision to have someone in that pivotal position who had been involved, from day one, in discussions about these issues. As an added bonus to being fluently bilingual, Bérard had worked with universities and a provincial licensing board, so he was proficient in both their "languages" as well.

John Barr was named Registrar Emeritus upon his retirement and one of his major undertakings was to organize the celebrations for the Council's 75th Anniversary in 1987, and these were deemed "a class act" by all in attendance. The Minister of National Health and Welfare, the Honourable Jake Epp, shown here with Daniel Snidal, was one of many guests of honour, which included past Presidents and retirees, including Alice Wilcox who travelled from her home on Vancouver Island for the occasion.

The Council had been evaluating its candidates through a written comprehensive qualifying examination since 1980. Its first three papers, called Q1, Q2 and Q3, used multiple-choice questions to test a candidate's knowledge, with the fourth, Q4, made up of patient management problems. The latter had fallen into disrepute and was a flashpoint of discontent. Many of the provincial licensing boards and universities were increasingly dissatisfied with the fact that while the Council's examinations measured a candidate's knowledge, they did not test what he or she might do in an actual clinical situation, while evaluation specialists at the McLaughlin Centre were concerned about the validity and reliability of the Q4 results. There was widespread pressure for the Council to upgrade and widen its evaluation process to offer an acceptable qualification for licensure in the 1990s.

By 1987 there were three Council initiatives converging on solutions. The Future Directions Task Force, chaired by Dale Dauphinee, had just been set in motion. The aim was to arrive at national standards based on clearly defined evaluation objectives, which was the focus of another task force, and to find the best tools for a national examination of clinical skills, which was the bailiwick of the Q4 Research Project. Everyone realized that it would be no easy task, given the complexity of the educational, regulatory, logistical and financial aspects of the many-sided problem.

Despite all this positive movement forward, a low point came that same year, at the 75th anniversary meeting when the celebration was dampened appreciably by the news relayed by Augustin Roy that Quebec had just legislated a requirement that doctors wishing to practise in that province would have to pass a special provincial examination that included a clinical competence examination for general practice. This meant the licentiate would not be recognized in Quebec – a damaging blow to the Medical Council, whose raison d'être since its founding had been to establish a qualification in medicine acceptable to all provinces for the issuance of a licence to practise within their boundaries. Worse, the Quebec decision was only the tip of the iceberg, and there was widespread questioning of the relevance and the need for the Council and its examinations. As the saying goes, "There's nothing like a hanging to focus the mind," and the Council got very focused, very quickly.

With the help of The Honourable E. W. Barootes, past President (1972-1973) and now Senator, the Council held its 75th annual meeting at the Parliament Buildings, where the first meeting had convened in 1912. They even replicated the pose of the first Council on the steps in front of Centre Block. At nearly seven feet in height, President Daniel P. Snidal (front row, centre) towers over the new Registrar, Michel Bérard to his left and Vice-President Jacques Des Marchais to his right.

The Council's first meeting in 1912 and its 75ᵗʰ in 1987 (shown here) took place in the ornate splendour of the Parliament Buildings. In between, they were held originally in private apartments provided by the Grand Trunk Railway in the Ottawa train station, until they were moved across the street to the more up-scale comforts of the Château Laurier, which became the preferred meeting spot for much of the Council's history. Meetings ended with the singing of the national anthem well into the 1940s, and the roll call, which started each day of the meeting, was only recently dropped. The roll call was instituted in 1912 so the Registrar could keep track of which members had turned up to earn their per diem.

11. TRANSFORMED AGAIN

T he preliminary report of the Future Directions Task Force, tabled in 1988, recommended a complete overhaul of the Council's qualifying examination. Its Q1, Q2 and Q3 papers were to be kept, but updated in line with the new evaluation objectives. The Q4 paper was to be totally replaced by one that better evaluated clinical decision-making. Plus, the single comprehensive format was to be changed back to a two-part examination, with the second part to be a completely new examination that would assess basic clinical competence not measurable by written questions. The Task Force's final report in 1989 suggested major changes to how the Council functioned, most notably that it should develop its own in-house examination centre. These recommendations were all accepted, and their implementation was to occupy the Medical Council well into the 1990s. And, as is true when traditional ways go through a transformation, it was not always an easy passage.

The qualifying examination was being rebuilt from the ground up. In the mid-1980s a task force, led by Daniel Snidal, had looked at the basic question of "what" the examination was to evaluate, as the first step to defining "how" it should be redesigned to reach that goal. The objectives that they developed were approved by Council in 1988, and handed over to Louis Levasseur and John Baumber for refinement into a blueprint for the setting of the examination. This was accomplished through extensive consultation with the medical schools and provincial licensing boards, as well as through a lot of hard work by the test committees and a team at the University of Calgary. By 1991, the objectives had been integrated into the Q1, Q2 and Q3 papers, and the first edition of "Objectives for the Qualifying Examination" was published in 1992. The book was viewed as the Council's first public response to the pressure to upgrade and extend its evaluation process. Baumber was clear in his introduction that it was written specifically "for those who have the task of writing evaluation questions for purposes of certifying medical competence;" however, it was also an extremely useful study guide in that it outlined precisely the Council's expectations for the knowledge, skills and attitudes of candidates for the licentiate. As a result the publication was a positive step toward countering a wave of rising student anxiety and opposition to the new, improved examination.

Licentiate to Heal:
A History of the
Medical Council
of Canada

Work on the in-house examination centre was also progressing rapidly. By the time the McLaughlin Centre moved to Ottawa in 1987, it was carrying out a much-reduced workload for the Council – basically just storing the bank of questions developed by the Council's test committees and scoring the examinations. With the luxury of space in its new office, the Council was now able to forge ahead with its plan. From as early as 1988, the Medical Council had been repatriating its bank of examination questions from the Centre. In 1991, David Blackmore, the first director of the Council's new Evaluation Bureau was hired, and by 1992 a staff with the necessary expertise was in place and operations were up and running. The 18-year connection with the McLaughlin Centre was severed amicably at year-end. For the first time since the 1960s, the Council was in complete control of it evaluation process. By 1993, the administrative burden of handling the applications for the examinations was formalized and pulled together into another new group, with Noreen Nolan as the Council's first director of Credentials and Registration.

Michel J. Bérard became the seventh Registrar in 1987, at a time when the Medical Council was under siege, with the real possibility that it would disappear from lack of support from its constituents: the provincial licensing boards and the universities. Under Bérard, who had an unshakeable belief in the absolute necessity for the Medical Council, this situation started to turn around. The organization was overhauled and relocated to its own building, the examinations upgraded, and the in-house Evaluation Bureau set up. Bérard's appointment was also the first time a Council member had become Registrar, a trend that has continued to this day. He had joined the Council in 1978 as a representative of the Corporation Professionelle des médecins du Québec. He served as President for only 69 days before stepping down to tackle the challenges of the Registrar position. Upon retirement, Bérard was named Registrar Emeritus.

On April 6, 1990, the Medical Council moved into its very own home. After much debate, the Council bought space in a new office condominium at 2283 St. Laurent Boulevard. Originally, it occupied only part of the third floor, but by 2004 the Council had purchased the entire three-story building at bargain basement prices owing to a slump in the Ottawa real estate market. The Medical Council now occupies the entire building except for a suite on the ground floor occupied by the Federation of Medical Regulatory Authorities of Canada.

The Q4 Research Project, which the Council had taken over from the McLaughlin Centre in 1986, with Ian Bowmer as its director, was making great strides toward developing a better way to test a candidate's clinical decision-making skills. The new approach, championed by its principal investigators, Georges Bordage and Gordon Page, was based on short clinical scenarios that focused on unique challenges, or "key features", followed by two or three questions that assessed critical decisions and actions in the resolution of the problem, not the underlying knowledge. The Q4 test committee, chaired by Ian Holmes, put in a massive effort to refine the questions, align them with the new objectives, and field-test them. In 1991, sample questions were included for the first time as a pilot test in the qualifying examination. In 1992, the new Q4 questions completely replaced the old patient management problems.

In September 1989, the Q5 Nucleus Committee, led by Richard Reznick, started to develop the new competency-based examination recommended by the Future Directions Task Force. Q5, which became Part II of the qualifying examination, was designed to measure clinical skills and attitudes through the use of an "Objective Structured Clinical Examination," which used people trained to simulate a particular clinical situation. It was a radical concept and a costly undertaking, in that hundreds of trained and paid "patients" would be required to run the examination for over 2,000 candidates a year. A dramatic hands-on demonstration at the 1990 annual meeting, in which Council members were the candidates interacting with the "patient," clinched the deal, and a successful pilot test was carried out in February of the next year. The new Part II was offered at two sites in October 1992, and was taken by 402 candidates, of whom 91% passed. The next year it ran at seven centres, with over 1,351 candidates.

Underpinning all these initiatives was a very pointed communications campaign about why the Council had been established and its unique role in the continuum of medical qualification in Canada. The Council had traditionally gone about its business and maintained a low profile, and many considered this to be one of the reasons for the current crisis of confidence. As one response, the newsletter *Echo* was started up in January 1989. Edited by the First Vice-President, it was low-cost but effective means of keeping everyone informed between meetings. The Registrar and key Council members also embarked upon a vigorous program of external liaison with other organizations to "sell" the concept of the new examinations to some and ease the concerns of others.

"... the new examinations were putting
the Medical Council firmly at the forefront
of evaluation development."

With the purchase of their own office space, a bigger staff, more test committees, more examiners, and the costs for developing the new examinations topping a million dollars, money was flying out the door. The finance committee, accustomed to carefully tending the slow but sure growth of the nest egg, was understandably jittery. The Council's funding came solely from the examination fees, and between 1988 and 1992 they had to be hiked three times to cover the mounting costs, and grants and cost-sharing options were explored with some success. A Research and Development Fund was created in 1992, with the idea that the Council's contribution could be supplemented by external bodies and fundraising. To enable this, the Council sought and was granted registration as a charity, so as to offer tax receipts for any personal or corporate donations.

Momentum was building at a dizzying speed, and the new examinations were putting the Medical Council firmly at the forefront of evaluation development. Best of all, the universities and the licensing boards, with the exception of Quebec, had finally agreed on national standards for physicians, as outlined in a landmark joint statement put out by the Association of Canadian Medical Colleges, the Federation of Medical Licensing Authorities of Canada and the Medical Council in 1991. It stated that after January 1, 1994, the successful completion of the Council's two-part qualifying examination would be a prerequisite for licensure to practise in a province. Another breakthrough was the equally longed-for elimination of the provincial licensing boards' enabling certificates, which had previously been a requirement to write the Council's examination and which had caused so much difficulty over the years owing to the uneven standards set for them by the different provinces. At the 1992 annual meeting, Bérard, the shepherd of so much of this change, announced his retirement, and the search for the eighth Registrar resulted in the hiring of Dale Dauphinee, a 20-year veteran of the Council.

Louis Levasseur (right), after 20 years as chair of the Examination Board and Central Examination Committee, retired the same year as his good friend and ally Bérard (left). John Baumber, Levasseur's partner in the development of the examination objectives, paid tribute to him as the unselfish, dedicated "workhorse" of the Council, and attributed to him much credit for the transformation of the examination. In honour of his commitment and achievement, the Louis Levasseur Award was established in 1998 to recognize outstanding contributions to the Council. Fittingly, Michel Bérard was its first recipient and John Baumber its second. The Levasseur Award is a framed painting of the Roddick Gates.

Over the years, there have been many instances of long serving Council members, but less than a handful could match Joe Josephson, who joined the Council as a member in 1956 and retired after the 1990 meeting. Josephson was originally a Governor-in-Council appointee, later becoming the representative of the Newfoundland licensing board. He was President for the 1965-1966 term.

12. INTO *the* 21st CENTURY

B y the time Dale Dauphinee took up his new position in late 1993, the Medical Council had pretty much completed its extreme makeover. It had suffered through a particularly bad mid life crisis, and reversed its fortunes by going out and buying itself a new office, establishing its own sophisticated examination centre, and building a new examination that was to win kudos around the world. It had a stronger buy-in from many of its university and licensing board members to the concept of a portable national qualification in medicine, and had shed its low-profile image. Indeed, the initial firestorm of opposition to the new examination had forced the Council to hold a public debate through the media and through meetings with all parts of the medical community. The transformation was apparent even in the fine detail, with the tradition-steeped title of Registrar modernized to Executive Director to reflect the much-expanded scope of the position.

One of Dauphinee's first jobs was to implement the recommendations of the Task Force on Governance and Management, chaired by Dennis A. Kendel, that had looked at all aspects of Council operations. A key recommendation set the groundwork for a more empowered and accountable membership. The task force urged a new approach to appointing the representatives of the universities and provinces to ensure that they brought to the table the views of their organization and, on the flip side of the coin, carried back the issues and decisions of the Council for discussion and action. For the universities this meant their appointee would have to be linked to the dean's office, and for the licensing boards, one of the two would be the Registrar, breaking a longstanding tradition that Registrars attended only as observers.

As well, the task force recommended inviting the Northwest Territories and the Yukon each to send two representatives of their licensing boards, and medical students and residents to appoint a representative each – all joined in 1995. Aligned medical organizations were also granted non-voting associate membership. An even more dramatic change came from the government's decision to opt out of making the three Governor-in-Council appointments, leaving it to the Council to come up with an alternative. The decision was to reserve these slots, with provision for an additional two, for lay members to represent the public. The first members-at-large, Rita Bakan, Monique Jérôme-Forget and Louise Simard, joined the Council in November 1996. In 2006, more change would bring the Council to its current complement of 48, with the addition of a representative of the Northern Ontario School of Medicine and two for Nunavut. These new viewpoints at the table have added a vital new dimension to Council debate and stronger validity to its decisions.

The prickliest issue to emerge in the 1990s involved the harmonization of the Council's qualifying examination with those of other examining bodies. A task force set up in 1993, led by Douglas Wilson, worked with all the various groups in Canada's licensing community toward the very ambitious goal of developing an acceptable plan for coordinating the evaluation and assessment processes prior to licensure. While the will was there, the negotiations were long and arduous, and the details of implementation kept bogging down any hope of consensus. In 1996, the matter was put on hold while the Federation of Medical

---

W. Dale Dauphinee became the eighth Registrar on December 16, 1993, bringing a wealth of experience and knowledge from his two decades on Council as McGill's representative. He had been President in 1978-1979 and had worked tirelessly on numerous committees, notably chairing the influential Future Directions Task Force that was to reconfigure and revitalize the Council's examination process. His title was changed to Executive Director in 1994 to reflect the true nature of his position at the helm of the much larger and more complex organization that the Medical Council had become in the 1990s. Dauphinee's stature as a leader in evaluation was underscored by his being selected as the 1997 recipient of the National Board of Medical Examiners' prestigious John P. Hubbard Award, given to recognize significant contributions in that field.

The Council examinations have been held in spite of many external challenges over the years, but none more serious than the SARS crisis. Colin D'Cunha, the Deputy Registrar of the spring 2003 examinations in Toronto, was Ontario's Chief Medical Officer of Health at the time and in the hot seat for managing the crisis. With the original site, Princess Margaret Hospital, off limits, he found another examination centre for the candidates in a no-longer-used school building, which had to be specially outfitted as a clinical examination centre. D'Cunha, shown during one of his daily SARS briefings for the media, received a special certificate of appreciation from the Council for his extraordinary effort.

Licensing Authorities of Canada came to grips with dissenting views within its membership. The Council, meanwhile, continued to pursue some of the sub-goals, notably, aligning its Part II qualifying examination to a common time period with other groups. There was a particularly welcome development in Quebec, where the final examinations for family medicine included the College of Family Physicians of Canada examination and a Collège des médecins du Québec clinical competence examination specific for family medicine, with the Council's Part II being optional. In 2000, the Collège decided to include Part II as a component of its clinical competence examination for family medicine, and in 2001 the first conjoint examinations between the Council and the Collège took place. In October 2006, the Collège decided to remove its requirement for a specific Quebec examination, basing the examination part of its licensure requirements in family medicine on the College of Family Physicians of Canada examination and both parts of the Council's qualifying examination.

Ironic though it may seem, flowing from the harmonization exercise to streamline the many different examinations was the realization that yet another examination was needed to assess a candidate's knowledge of the legal, ethical issues and organizational aspects of contemporary medical practice. There was such consensus on this point that, even though the overarching discussion about harmonization still raged, the Council and the Federation of Medical Licensing Authorities of Canada set up a joint committee in 1996 to block out the objectives for this new examination that came to be known by its acronym CLEO (Considerations of the Legal, Ethical and Organizational aspects of medicine). In the early days of development there was talk of making CLEO a separate part of the qualifying examination, a Part III; but, in the end, it was decided to fully integrate its components into both parts of the existing examination, with the first CLEO-enhanced examination run in 2000. Communications skills and cultural awareness were added to the mix shortly thereafter. This expanded version, known as C_2LEO (the C_2 standing for Cultural-Communications) was developed in 2005 and its integration into the examination will start in 2008.

The Council's examination questions, through the work of the test committees, undergo a continual process of re-evaluation and refinement to keep pace with rapidly evolving medical knowledge, evaluation methodology and technology. The objectives that form the blueprint for the questions are revised regularly as well, with the 3rd edition released online in 2003. Efficiencies in administering the examinations and ease of access for the candidates are constant goals as well. A good example is illustrated by the evolution of the original Part II examination, which was very time intensive, involving 20 different stations each with its own trained "patient" and a physician-examiner to mark the candidate. It was expensive to run, and candidates were objecting to the high examination fees needed to recoup costs. Different approaches were tested, with a decision in 1998 to simply cut the number of stations to 14. As a result, fees were reduced by $200, the examination cut to one day from two, and the Council was able to open three more testing centres making the examination more accessible to candidates.

One of the most revolutionary changes was the move to computer-based examinations, and, in 1996, Council gave the Evaluation Bureau the go-ahead to explore the conversion of the multiple-choice questions of Part I of the qualifying examination to computer-adaptive testing methodologies. David Blackmore took a working sabbatical at centres of expertise such as the University of Alberta and the National Board of Medical Examiners to develop prototypes. Pilot testing began as early as 1997, with a full-scale practice examination at 16 sites in May 2000 to "proof the infrastructure." It was a clear success, and the Council's first completely computer-administered examination ran in November 2000 at 13 universities. This surprisingly smooth transition was derailed, momentarily, the next year by a plague of computer glitches involving delays in the transmission of examination materials and a complete server breakdown, requiring massive crisis management by Council staff. These wrinkles were all successfully ironed out, and future examinations went like clockwork. The benefits were huge: shorter, customized examinations, faster results and reduced costs, to name but a few.

R.M. Louise Simard was one of the first public members appointed to the Council in 1996, and she was the first public member to become President, 2002-2003. She has an impressive background in law and politics, culminating in 1991 with a five-year stint as the Minister of Health for Saskatchewan, during the complete restructuring of its health care system.

In the late 1990s, the Council embarked upon another broad-based assessment, similar to the future directions task force of the previous decade. The "visioning" exercise, led by Larry R. Ohlhauser, involved an intense commitment from Council members and staff, and extensive consultation with other groups in the continuum of medical licensure in Canada about their perceptions of the Council, its services, products and role. In such an undertaking, the journey is as important as the destination, and the resulting vision and mission statements were the distillation of the discussions along the way. Adopted in 2001, they constitute the guiding code that the Council works under and strives for, and both are displayed prominently in Council literature. These statements were complemented and fleshed out, in 2003, by the enunciation of six strategic goals, which covered the Council's traditional mandate (providing qualification for the licentiate and maintaining the Canada Medical Register), recent additions (increased liaison with other bodies responsible for assessment and evaluation and R&D in those fields), new initiatives (a national integrated assessment strategy of physicians throughout their careers), and management style (open, transparent, responsive and accountable).

Dauphinee retired after a 13-year stint as Executive Director, and his successor, Ian Bowmer, started on January 1, 2007. Under Bowmer's leadership, the Medical Council is continuing its long tradition of innovation in the ongoing evolution of its examinations, adapting them to changes in medicine, evaluation methodology and delivery mechanisms. A major project will see the Council's evaluating examination, which assesses the prior medical knowledge of international medical graduates, switch from a written to a computer-based format by 2008. Collaboration with Australia to develop a common evaluating examination, recognized by both countries, will result in further economies of scale and benefits from the sharing of expertise.

page 84

∞

Licentiate to Heal:
A History of the
Medical Council
of Canada

The Council's new Executive Director, M. Ian Bowmer, earned his stripes as a Council member representing Memorial University of Newfoundland and Labrador from 1981 to 1992. He served as President, 1990-1991, and was involved in the development of the Council's original objectives that now form the blueprint for its examinations and of the groundbreaking Q4 examination that tests a candidate's clinical reasoning skills. An internationally renowned researcher in infectious diseases, educator and physician, Bowmer took up the position on January 1, 2007. His challenge will be to keep the Medical Council at the forefront of medical evaluation in today's constantly shifting environment.

Today's Medical Council of Canada is, in so many ways, light years away from the one-man operation and single examination of almost one hundred years ago. Now with over 60 staff, its own in-house evaluation and examination centre, a modern office building, dynamic research and development programs, and sophisticated examinations administered to over 11,000 candidates annually, it would be an utter revelation to its founders. Similarly, the Council now manoeuvres through a world unimaginable to them – with a complexity that has increased a hundredfold since 1912 and with advances in medicine occurring at a head-spinning pace.

Where Thomas Roddick and his colleagues would feel right at home, though, is at the Council's boardroom table, which continues to be the unique meeting ground for medical educators and the licensing authorities – the two groups who must work in tandem to fulfil their basic mandate, which is to ensure for Canadians a high standard of competence in their physicians. The Medical Council of Canada remains the vital enabling link between the two communities to this day, just as Roddick envisioned it.

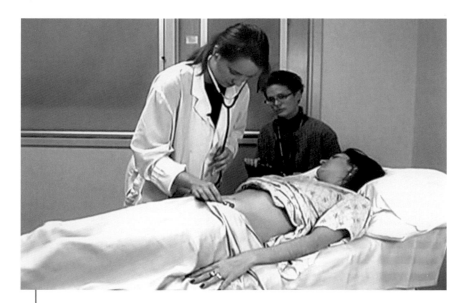

As part of the two-part examination for a Medical Council of Canada licentiate, examiners measure a candidate's clinical skills and attitudes by observing how he or she interacts with a person trained to simulate a particular clinical situation.

SELECTED READING

The minutes of the annual meetings of the Medical Council of Canada are a superb source of information. They were published in various configurations, starting as early as 1914, under various titles: "Annual Announcement," "Minutes and Proceedings" and "Annual Report."

Andison, A.W and Robichon, J.G. (editors). *The Royal College of Physicians and Surgeons of Canada, Fiftieth Anniversary*. St. Anne de Bellevue: Harpell's Co-operative Press, 1979.

Barr, J.W.B. *Medical Council of Canada*, reprint of nine part series, CMA Journal, commencing July 20, 1974.

Dauphinee, W.D. *Licences, examinations and more examinations*. CMAJ 1991: 144 (8), April 15, 1991, p. 967-969

Jack, D. *Rogues, Rebels and Geniuses: The Story of Canadian Medicine*. Toronto: Doubleday Canada Limited, 1981.

Heagerty, J.J. *Four Centuries of Medical History in Canada and a Sketch of the Medical History of Newfoundland*. Toronto: The Macmillan Company of Canada, 1928.

Kerr, R.B. *History of the Medical Council of Canada*. Victoria, BC: Morriss Printing Company Ltd., 1979.

MacDermot, H.E. *Sir Thomas Roddick: His Work in Medicine and Public Life*. Toronto: The Macmillan Company of Canada, 1938.

MacDermot, H.E. *One Hundred Years of Medicine in Canada (1867-1967)*. Toronto/Montreal: McClelland and Stewart Limited, 1967.

MacDermot, H.E. *History of the Canadian Medical Association*. Toronto: Murray Printing Company Limited, 1935.

RESEARCH NOTES

The story of the Medical Council has been pieced together from many sources. In addition to published materials, some of which are listed in "Selected Reading," correspondence, verbatim minutes of meetings and other primary documents that reside in the files of the Medical Council's headquarters and in the Medical Council of Canada Fonds at Library and Archives Canada were used extensively.

Another important source was transcripts of interviews that Robert Card conducted with some 30 key players in the Council's later history. These provided valuable background information and personal recollections about the Council's key issues and daily operations, many of which went back well into the 1970s and a few even earlier. The Council's newsletter "Echo," which was published starting in January 1989, was another good source for the more recent years.

For those wishing to pursue the precise sources of material in the text, a fully annotated manuscript of this book, showing all references and including the complete bibliography, is on file at the Council's headquarters.

PHOTO CREDITS

Canadian Medical Association: page 3.
Canadian War Museum: page 18.
Library and Archives Canada: page 4, 15 and 29.
McGill Archives: page 9, 32 and all cover photos except Council building.
Royal College of Physicians and Surgeons of Canada: page 26 (WWI), 41 and 50.
Toronto Star: page 80.
Robert Card: page 36 (snow plane).
Tracy Carefoot: page 95.
David Blackmore: page 38, 52 and 72.

All other images are from the Medical Council of Canada.

ACKNOWLEDGEMENTS

The author is grateful for the ongoing support of Ian Bowmer throughout this project and for the invaluable assistance of many Council staff, notably: David Blonde, David Blackmore, Shirley Brown, Andrée Fortin-Bélanger, Jessica Hertzog, Lise Martineau, Susan McHarg, Sydney Smee, Carole White and Josée Wojcik. A very special thanks goes to Robert Card whose advice and comprehensive knowledge of the Council's history were critical to interpreting the story of the Council's more recent years.

The archivists at two other institutions were extremely helpful and generous in loaning images and reference materials: Tammi Boales of the Royal College of Physicians and Surgeons of Canada and Kerry Guglielmin of the Canadian Medical Association.

The insightful comments of the reviewers of the text were particularly appreciated, and a thank you goes to each of them: Ian Bowmer, Robert Card, Elizabeth Hillman, Dennis Kendel, Glen McIver, Robert Young and Pamela Walsh. Another special thank you goes to Sylvie Leboeuf of the Collège des médecins du Québec for reviewing the French translation.

INDEX

"The Council" refers to the Medical
Council of Canada. Bold numbers
indicate illustrations or captions.

O

"Objectives for the Qualifying
     Examination", 70
office buildings, 33, **38**, 44, **52**, 64, 74, 77
Ohlhauser, Larry R., 84
Ontario, 17, **21**, 28, 38, 78

P

Page, Gordon, 73
Parliament Buildings, **21**, **67**, **68**
pediatrics, 48
planning, 66, 69, 73, **78**, 84
Powell, Robert, 20, 22, **23**, 31, 33
pre-Confederation practice, 1, 5
Presidents
     depicted, **21**, **26**, **50**, **67**, **76**, **78**, **82**, **84**
     Honourary, 24
     names of, 19, 34, **36**, 37, 58, 60
preventive medicine, 58
Prince Edward Island, 7, 11, 16
Province of Canada, 5
provinces
     enabling certificates, 38, 58, 74
     licences, 14, 28, 37-38, 60, 66
     licensing boards, 19, 37-38, 69, **70**, 74,
          76, 78, 81
     representatives on the Council, 77-78
     See also individual provinces
psychiatry, 51
public health, 14, 58
public members *See* lay members
publicity, 27-28, 31, 73, 77, 84

Q

Q4 Research Project, 66, 69, 73, **84**
Q5 Nucleus Committee, 73
qualifying examinations, 60, 70, 78
Quebec, 17, **21**, 66, 81
Quebec City, 5
Queen's University, 37

R

R. Samuel McLaughlin Foundation, 57
R.S. McLaughlin Examination and
     Research Centre, 57-58, 61, 64, 70
reciprocity, international, 14, 22, 28
Registrar Emeritus, 63, **66**
Registrars
     depicted, **35**, **46**, **55**, **56**, **67**, **70**, **75**, **78**
     named, 20, 31, 33-34, **46**, 47, 53, **57**, 63,
          64, 74
     promotional activities, 73
     retirement of title, 77
     See also Honourary Registrars
registration *See* Canada Medical Register
registration without examination, 2, 17, 22,
     23, 25. *See also* ten-year clause
Research and Development Fund, 74
research into licensure and assessment, 54,
     57, 64, 74. *See also* Q4 Research Project
Reznick, Richard, 73
Roche, W.J., 19, 22, **30-31**
Roddick, Amy Redpath, 25, **32**
Roddick Memorial Gates, **32**, **75**
Roddick, Thomas George
     death of, 31
     depicted, **9**, **10**, **21**, **50**
     as member of Parliament, 12, 13-14, 16-17
     name in the Canada Medical Register, 22
     as President, 19, 24
     recognition of, 24, 27, **32**, **50**
     in retirement, 24, 25, 27
Roulcau, Roger, 53, **54-55**
Roy, Augustin, 66
Royal College of Physicians and Surgeons
     of Canada, 37, **50**, 51, 57, 58
Royal Commission on Health Services, 48-49
Ryerson, E. Stanley, **36**, 37, 40, **41**

*Licentiate to Heal:
A History of the
Medical Council
of Canada*